D1252637

A Week
in Robert's World:
THE SOUTH

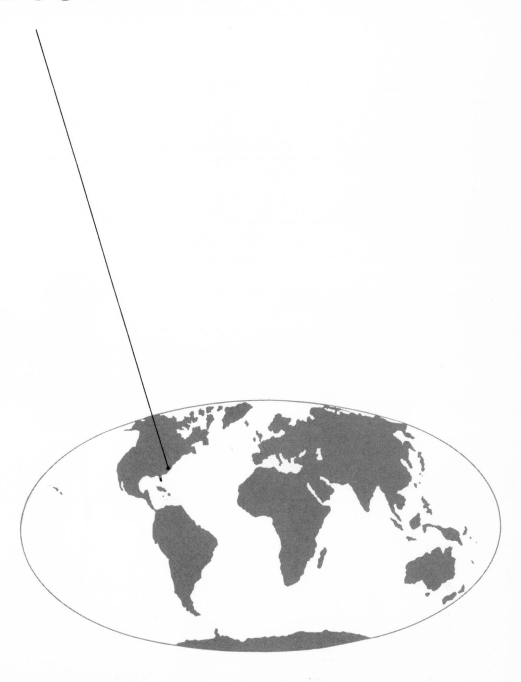

CROWELL-COLLIER PRESS

Collier-Macmillan Limited, London

A Week in Robert's World: THE SOUTH

Photographs by Bruce Roberts
Text by Nancy Roberts

Photographs from Rapho Guillumette Pictures

Robert Lee Harris lives in the small town of Huntersville, North Carolina. It is Monday morning and time to leave for school. While he waits for his sisters, he watches the wind making the fall leaves twist and dance.

"You don't want to go to school with jelly on your shirt," says Daddy.

Robert Lee strides happily down the red clay road
to meet his school bus. He is in the first grade.

Robert Lee watches his teacher, Mrs. McGinn, write a list of new words on the blackboard. When she finishes, he will make up sentences with the words.

Robert Lee enjoys reading aloud in class. He also likes to try to read signs along the road when he rides in Daddy's car.

There are many kinds of trees on the school playground. Among them are hickory, sweet gum, pine, oak and poplar. "I wonder what kind of tree this leaf came from," says Robert Lee. "It's an oak leaf," Mrs. McGinn tells him.

"Over you go!" says
Robert Lee's friend Teddy.

Robert Lee jumps from the school bus and almost stumbles. He is in such a hurry to get home and play! But first he gets the newspaper for Mother from the mailbox at the side of the road. Then with two of his big sisters, Carol and Jan, he starts toward home. Cynthia, his oldest sister, comes home later. She takes the high school bus.

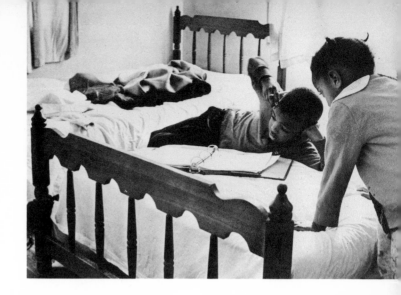

Mother has a job two mornings a week. But every day after school she makes sure she is home with cold milk and cookies for Robert Lee.

Robert Lee's little sister, Annette, wants him to play with her. "Not now," he tells her. "I have to study my spelling."

If Daddy is home Robert Lee helps him after school. They rake up leaves and clean the yard together. "These old boards will make good firewood," says Daddy.

When work is done, Robert Lee visits his friend
Aubrey. Aubrey has a pony named Beauty. The
boys take turns riding Beauty. Robert Lee wishes
he had his own pony. If he did, he would gallop
like the wind.

Today in school the children can make
anything they want to out of clay. Robert
Lee starts to make an animal. But then he
decides to make a man instead. Mrs.
McGinn asks him who the man is. "It's
my Daddy!" says Robert Lee.

Mother has said he can go down-town all by himself after school. There she will pick him up and take him home.

On the main street of Huntersville, Robert Lee asks Officer Cook, "How does that stop light work without anybody touching it?" Officer Cook tells him, "It works on electricity. It stays one minute on red and one minute on green." The policeman is there to help the children cross safely.

Later, Robert Lee plays in a corn-field. The long rows of cornstalks make a fine, shadowy place for games of hide-and-seek. Jan is hiding. She thinks Robert Lee can't find her. But his sharp eyes see her.

"What is in this old barn?"
wonders Robert Lee. Maybe a
monster is up in the loft. He
looks hard, but he can see only
a spider web and lots of dust.
The straw smells musty.

It is almost supper time. Robert
Lee runs home through the pine
trees. The fallen needles feel
springy under his feet. He sniffs
the good smell of the pine trees.

On Saturday, Mother takes Robert Lee and Annette
with her to shop at Ransom's Grocery. Robert Lee
likes to help Mother decide what to buy. "I'd like pork
chops," says Robert Lee. "Chicken for me," says
Annette. Mother orders both pork chops and chicken.

Saturday afternoon is just for playing. Robert Lee plays
follow-the-leader with Jan and Annette. Annette tries to do
everything her big brother does. But Robert Lee is hard to
keep up with. Then he climbs the tallest pine tree near
his house. He likes to feel high above the whole world.

On Sunday morning, Robert Lee goes to
the Baptist Church with his family. After
the service is over, he stops and says,
"Good morning," to Reverend Heath.

Once upon a time the people of the church used this old well. But water has not been drawn from it for a long time.

While Mother cooks dinner,
Robert Lee helps to tidy up
the front porch. Then he looks
at a bird book with Annette.
"Was that a mockingbird in
the yard?" he wonders.

At last! Sunday dinner is
on the table. Mother
serves fried chicken,
potato salad, sliced toma-
toes and hot cornbread.
Cynthia is sitting next to
Mother so she can help
with the serving. Daddy
says the blessing, and
everyone begins to eat.

The scoutmaster, who lives next door, comes to call after dinner. "I can hardly wait to join the Cub Scouts," Robert Lee tells him.

During the week Daddy has two jobs. He works part of each day as the maintenance man at a nearby school. In the afternoon he goes to work at a foam rubber mill. But on Sunday afternoon, Daddy plays with the children.

Daddy also shows Robert Lee how to take care of his toys. There are so many things to do together when Daddy is home.

Robert Lee often goes to visit his grandparents on Sunday afternoons. Today is a very special Sunday. It is Robert Lee's birthday, and he is seven years old.

Annette, Jan and Robert Lee wait for Grand-
mother to light the candles on the cake.
"Chocolate is my favorite kind," he tells her.

Robert Lee wishes hard for a pony of his very own.

Oh, oh! One candle will not
go out. But Robert Lee wants
that pony! He huffs and puffs,
and the last candle goes out.

He has eaten so much cake
and ice cream! It feels good
just to sit with Grandfather
and watch television. Grandfather tells him all about the
game of football.

Robert Lee is very tired, but he is trying to catch just one fish before dark. Soon the long Sunday will be over, and a new week will begin.